THE POW POETRY

BULLYING

ENVIRONMENT

EQUALITY

YOUR FUTURE

HOPE

CHANGE

CONFLICT

YOUR DREAMS

IDENTITY

REFLECTIONS ON LIFE

EDITED BY DEBBIE KILLINGWORTH

First published in Great Britain in 2023 by:

 Young**Writers**

Young Writers
Remus House
Coltsfoot Drive
Peterborough
PE2 9BF
Telephone: 01733 890066
Website: www.youngwriters.co.uk

Printed and bound in the UK by BookPrintingUK
Website: www.bookprintinguk.com
YB0554F

FOREWORD

Since 1991, here at Young Writers we have celebrated the awesome power of creative writing, especially in young adults where it can serve as a vital method of expressing their emotions and views about the world around them. In every poem we see the effort and thought that each student published in this book has put into their work and by creating this anthology we hope to encourage them further with the ultimate goal of sparking a life-long love of writing.

Our latest competition for secondary school students, **The Power of Poetry,** challenged young writers to consider what was important to them and how to express that using the power of words. We wanted to give them a voice, the chance to express themselves freely and honestly, something which is so important for these young adults to feel confident and listened to. They could give an opinion, highlight an issue, consider a dilemma, impart advice or simply write about something they love. There were no restrictions on style or subject so you will find an anthology brimming with a variety of poetic styles and topics. We hope you find it as absorbing as we have.

We encourage young writers to express themselves and address subjects that matter to them, which sometimes means writing about sensitive or contentious topics. If you have been affected by any issues raised in this book, details on where to find help can be found at
www.youngwriters.co.uk/info/other/contact-lines

CONTENTS

Downfall

A beautiful day in 2050, Hannah needs supplies
London's as hot as Barcelona and the heat's still on the rise.
Wiping the sweat from her brow, Hannah steps outside
Sees some kids up on the street ('My god! They look fried!')
Upon reaching our future shops, Hannah enters smoothly
Takes a stroll down the aisle, does pick up some muesli
When she finishes her big shop she takes it to the till
But the self-service machine doesn't do her will
"You've taken too much food!" the AI did but say
"Put some food back on the shelves and come back here
and pay."
Hannah did as she was told, and took her food back home
And soon reached her eco-tower, letting out a groan
"I hate these food shortages," Hannah Creed did curse
And this situation will only get much worse!
I'm afraid she's very right, if you don't take action now
Save our Hannah's future, and in case you don't know how
Save the water, stop the waste (don't burn it, just saying)
Take the action, do it now, don't just stand there praying!
In the end, I am sorry, Hannah got blown up -
Right before she could even say, 'Hiya, guys, what's up?'
The world leaders had too much, they were eager for power
And so all of this craving turned them all so sour
They waged war at one another, and last of all
Putin got a nuclear bomb and that was our downfall.

Danielle Potts (12)

Stories To Tell

Questions.
They're thought-provoking, mind-hurting, stomach-churning.
They're anticipation, start of a conversation, finding truth an interrogation.
They're rhetoric, they answer themselves, yet answers they demand, a plea for people to understand.
They educate, liberate, they create new ideas.
They're the magnifying glass breaking down verbal analytics, and if all the world's a stage proclaim them theatre critics.
They're an eyebrow raised, a puzzled gaze, but no matter their form they are always, gateways to more information.
... Or maybe we're overcomplicating things.

People.
They're emotional, often sociable, sometimes conversational.
They're hardworking, inventions occurring, always learning.
They're damaging, an excess of packaging, constantly panicking.
They like education but they love liberation, masters of creation.
Humans are often in the wrong, they're mistake makers, and if all the world's a stage, you know it, they are merely players.
Many are accustomed to lying, some just surviving, others living day to day until it comes to retiring.

... Or maybe we're overcomplicating things... again.

Ordinary people you see on the daily, could be the dad with the newborn baby or the single red rose being given to the lady.
Or the elderly woman sat on the bus, with the grey hair who sits right there, behind the driver, has done since she retired.
Each day she walks with a cane, gets on all the same.
Above her, the Year 10 boy, with a ploy to get to the seat before his friends.
Every day they pay their fares and head upstairs.
He'll get off and go home to his mum.
She'll get off and go home to no one.

He'll get asked, "How was your day?" for the 600th time, to which he'll reply, "It was fine."
She'll make her tea and watch TV all the same, and no one's even asked her her name.

Every week on the bus she sits, with 76 years of laughter and tears hidden in the wrinkles on her skin.
In the creases of her hand is the knowledge to understand any situation she could be faced with.
A million different lessons she's learnt and can teach, yet sitting on that bus with 33 different people, the silence is never broken by speech.

Each person you meet has so much to tell, yet you don't even know that you've met them.
The man at the train station, full of information, a dispenser of education that school could never teach you.

The barista serving coffee does hockey as a hobby, the waitress serving food wishes she pursued it.

Your grandma has a first love, your mum has one too, and generations of stories and lessons all lead down to you.

So, questions give us answers, which make strangers into people.
See, everyone has stories to tell and they aren't that hard to find.
If we all asked questions a little more, and kept an open mind.

Lauren Brine (17)

Big Little Girls

There's this feeling I live with.
It is nestled in my ribcage sharing a bed with my heart.
We've been rooming for years, I still don't know its damn name.
It's the feeling of being too big for your coat but you like how it looks and how squeezed in you feel,
How little it makes you.
It's the empty feeling when your favourite roller coaster at the fair doesn't feel as high as you remember it being.
Too big for a child, not emotional enough to be a teen,
Too little to be an adult but I am everything at once because it's my job.
Why wouldn't it be?
I have no duty to serve but I know I have to be what I have been assigned or else what the hell am I supposed to do?
Besides, it's easy. It'll always be easy.
If I've no god and no duty, that is the only thing I have to believe in.
One singular truth.
That the world we live in is built on the backs of big little girls who got cheated out of their childhood like their mothers and aunts and sisters and grandmothers before them.
I have to believe being a big little girl in a world that is not kind is the price paid to be extraordinary.
Or else, what was it all for?
What was all this for?

Senai Lee (17)

Castles In The Air

Am I guilty?
As a black boy racism vilifies me,
Social media vultures calumniating black people online,
The articles run rampant with this stereotype I'm supposed
to be
But I don't want to be
One that I'm not,
Are you happy now,

They destroy me; I'm like a statue lying trunkless, contrarily
At the heart of this country, in this bustling cosmopolitan
(London)
One 360-degree swivel, and you can see architects of the
slave trade,
John Cass and William Beckford stand in the Guildhall,
Standing loud and proud, whilst I lie trunkless,

At night, I stargaze at my pitch-black ceiling, void of hope,
In a society where I have the confidence,
The confidence to confront bigotry,
I am a villain
I am deathly fearful,
But today, I choose for that fear to be but the precursor to
valour
Battle the injustice and the detriment this world nurtures
Condemn the ignorance it harbours
And change the fear that I as a 'villain' hold

I go to my 'safe haven'
This genie can grant me all the liberties the world has to offer she says,
My persecutors are criminally liable, I hear?
Potential charges of hate crime, I hear?
These sweet nothings whispered into my ear,
Here I am savouring a non-existent taste,
This taste turned into a smell that lingered,
My friends get a whiff of that sweet smell of destroying oppression,
But it became this odorous cloud of empty promises,
Our: hopes, wishes and dreams were denied instantaneously,
Just when I began building castles in the air
Reality plagued my faculties.

Time to scrap the fantasies:
I'm diminished, denigrated, and demeaned,
Starting small; a blank canvas,
Brushstroke after brushstroke,
Painting that canvas of darkness,
I live in that canvas of darkness,
Day by day, hour by hour,
I claw and clamber my way out, to no avail,

They snort and scowl in self-harming envy to my successes,
Bigots may vituperate me and persecute me,
But they cannot invalidate my black excellence.

I am not a villain,
I am not guilty.

Rufaro Ruziwa (15)

13, 14, 15

What were you wearing?

I'm not quite sure anymore
It all depends
On, which time you are talking about
The one when I had just turned 7,
And I was too young to understand what had happened.

Or the night before my 10th birthday,
My innocence: robbed of me long before.

Maybe you're asking about when I was 11,
When I was on my way to the park.

You're most likely talking about 13, 14 or 15.
When I was asking,
Pleading,
Begging,
Making my daily journey to school.
The one I take every day.
In the same clothes, I wear every day
That serves as a reminder
Of the not-so-clandestine future that awaits me.
The reality of womanhood,
That was thrust upon me too early

All these times, tragedies, timeless tales of woe
I only remember wearing my heart on my sleeve.

Marie Keenan (14)

Hues Of Our Dying Planet

Red:
The colour of love, the colour of hate
The colour our blood and planet bleeds.

Blue:
The colour of the devastated skies hung above
Our heads oblivious to what hath become.

Green:
The colour of luck, the colour of greed
The colour we see vanishing from sight
The colour we see fading from light
The colour we see dying in plight.

Grey:
Our monochromatic views on life
Our homogeneous attitude to what lies before us
Our lack of promise, our lack of purpose
Our lack of help in place of harm to our planet.

Black:
The shade of the starry night sky
The shade of saying goodbye
The shade of leaving our planet to die.

White:
What makes up our light
What makes up our soon-to-be-destroyed life

The light our planet will see if our ways are not scythed.

These are the hues of our dying planet
The hues of which our society has damaged
To the point of which return is unmanaged.
Our colours have died
Our climate has not thrived
Our cities have killed more than survived.

Society has murdered the planet
The planet of whom had no choice but to comply
Its colours fading from daylight
Red, blue, green, grey, black, white and the like
Suffering due to our destructive flight.

Yellow:
The colour of fake joy, the colour of false hope
The colour we look forward to, though it is dope.

Purple:
The colour of royalty reigning above us
Illusioning us to what lay before
Promising us there is 'so much more in store'.

Pink:
The love we 'show' to others
The love we restrain from nature
The love we cannot split, share, or separate.

These are the hues of our dying planet
The hues of which our society has damaged
The hues of which are being mismanaged
We should feel pain
We should feel shame
We should feel for Mother Nature who's lost
More than what we have
Yet we mock
Yet we talk
Yet we rumourise more than block.

Say why, oh why, do we allow such a monstrosity?
Surely, we can save this before it becomes an atrocity
Surely, we care for our home, our birthplace, our livelihood
For these are the hues of our dying planet.

Josef Dickson (15)

A Rift In The Environment

Why do you break us and never acknowledge your wrongs?
Our capacities are fading, and we are no longer strong,
It's all your fault, taking what's ours all for you,
Don't you know that we deserve to live too?

You could break down your older buildings, or use some other land,
Where there are none like us, how about the sand?
There, you could make wind turbines or solar-powered energy,
But no, you came here, and made us your enemy,

We give you oxygen, that helps you breathe and grow,
You take it for granted, and reap what we sow,
You don't let us stretch again, and leave us with a stump,
How would you feel if you looked down and saw a lump?

If you keep cutting us down there will be none of us left,
A lot of us are already gone, and you carried them away with heft,
So, we ask you again, stop cutting us down please,
For in the end, we keep you alive,
Because we are trees.

Diala Farmer (18)

They Were Her All, And She Was The 'They'

She was their refuge, yet no one was hers
She gave them what no one else could,
And in return, they gave her much worse
She comforted them and made them feel safe,
They only took from her though, never even once gave.

She seemed tired, yet no one seemed to notice
While she withdrew, they grew and rose like a lotus
She was too nice to say anything, they just took advantage of it
She needed her refuge, someone, who like her was ready to commit.

Someone who was there for her, completed her when she was drained
A safe place, a person she could rely on, where their support wasn't feigned
She needed her person, a home she could retreat to
Everyone needs a place they seek refuge, you might not think so, but even you too.

She finally found that person, she just needed to search deeper
And she knew it was not ever possible for this person to leave her
They were her shelter, her house, even more, her home

She knew from then on she'd never be alone.

Her definition of refuge was no longer 'a safe place or a sanctum'
It had been modified to 'anything that reminds her of them'
Her smiles became real and her innocent laughs genuine
As you see, if someone's your refuge, they love you no matter what state you're in.

This person now painted her past, present and future
And it would always be like that, just like centimetres on a ruler
It's funny, she sought her refuge, and it became a part of her
They gave her a unique feeling, had her wishing she'd met them sooner.

She was their refuge, now someone was hers
She gave them what no one else could, and in return, they never gave any worse
She comforted them and made them feel safe,
They did the same, whilst they took, they also gave.

She was her own refuge, she was the 'they', she found comfort in herself
I mean, who better to make us feel safer, when only we truly know ourselves
We should complete ourselves, other people should be there to add
If someone else completes you, it's just hidden now, but you'll still always be sad...

Abigail Ikuesan (13)

Descending Into Chaos

Most of the food in our local shops are full of s**t,
and we're told it's okay.
We're told if we avoid these foods, we aren't 'treating
ourselves', we're neglecting self-care.
We are told this, and when we are addicted to foods full of
sugars made in labs,
we are told it's our fault,
while they continue to overpopulate deprived places with an
array of fast-food chains.
We are encouraged to drink milk that can give us cancer,
by organisations that swear they want to better the public's
health.

They profit from our declining health.

And we sit here, hoping for our prime ministers and leaders
to make a change.
Make the change they always claim they will make.
We hang onto their words of hope for years and years.
And in return, they pass on rules to benefit themselves and
their peers from prestigious private schools.

When Macron increased the retirement age without a vote,
more police were suddenly out on the street with weapons.
What the hell is democracy?

They profit from destroying our planet,
releasing thousands of emissions
and make us feel bad if we buy single-use plastic.

We are perpetually lied to,
and as a result, we become divided as a species
who judge one another based on labels, as we do to cans of soup -
We fight each other if our opinions differ to the majority,
in order to feed our own ego,
our constant desire to be *right*,
while we ignore the real problems at hand.
Like the fact we can't even trust our news to stay unbiased,
not even the BBC.

We are manipulated and made addicted to our screens,
reduced to a few lines of computer code for dopamine.
We are continually distracted,
in search of ephemeral pleasures.

We are taught to not think,
to obey without question.
We are made desensitised to the b*****t going on around us.
We say it's just the way the world is,
forgetting the strength we hold in numbers,
in which politicians try to take away from us,
and pass on bills to restrict our right to protest.
What the hell is democracy?

Tatiana Macaulay (15)

Boys Will Be Boys

"Boys will be boys"
They say

So when boys in your class are offensive
There's no need to be apprehensive

"Boys will be boys"
Ah the infamous saying

So when they punch a hole in a wall
They're only playing

"Boys will be boys"
They laugh

So when a boy punches you in a park
They're just trying to ignite a spark

"Boys will be boys"
Is that what most people believe?

This is drilled into you from a young age
Is it to make you more naive?

"Boys will be boys"
Yes they will

Because you teach them that what they do is acceptable
Therefore making you more susceptible.

"Misogyny doesn't exist in modern-day"
They say

But why is it that you're belittled for having a hobby
That doesn't involve being on display

"Misogyny is a thing of the past!"
Ah the most invalidating line

So when you're told a boy's abuse meant he liked you
The misogyny didn't come through?

"Sexism ended years ago"
They add

Then why when you try to play video games
Do they assume you're bad?

"Misogyny has stopped already"
So they really believe that?

Like young girls aren't told that being hit equals love
Like they don't believe that as fact.

"Sexism isn't a thing anymore"
Yes it is.

Because we're still experiencing it
Are they just going to keep going until we reach our limit?

Madison Chaplin (15)

Life

The hate I have cannot be expressed,
The feelings I have make me more depressed.
She never gives us a break, the pressure she puts on us,
A phone went off and she made a big fuss.
She tells us to study, revise and be prepared,
But she drowns us in homework, she clearly doesn't care.
When we're almost at the top we can see the fresh air,
But before we know it we've sunk back down to the bottom alone and
without care.
She tells us to be quiet to silence our voices,
While doing this she's ripping away our choices.
They say our uniform is supposed to make no one feel left out,
But everyone is so upset all they want to do is shout
At the teachers the real facts,
Their students are tired, depressed and alone
But the teachers just act.
Like we're all okay, all just fine,
But they can't see what's beyond the line.
Well at least we can go home to our kind, loving family,
But now everyone is struggling emotionally, financially.
Children are getting more homework than ever,
And families are almost never together.
Parents are stressed, everything's expensive,

They're trying to make money, it's becoming obsessive.
But the teachers won't know this and they never will,
Yes they may be struggling but they're not the only ones
going through a hard time,
And they wonder while children are committing more
crimes.
Teachers can go home and have a glass of wine,
Even though children are going through a harder time.
The teachers say they understand but they don't,
And when we try to explain we tell them to listen but they
won't.
Teachers, "Sshhh just listen..."
It's not a competition.
We just want to be heard.

Ruby Reilly (11)

1%

The past, origins, identity,
Colonialism, DNA, heritage,
And world history.

The human race has a diverse story,
All different but yet so similar,
Suffocating ourselves in our own glory.

In the beginning we came from Africa,
99% similar, 1% unique,
And that 1% is the germ of our dilemma.

That 1% provokes the urge to fight,
To wage wars and genocides,
But why do we house so much spite?

That 1% tells our entire life story,
From our race to our families,
Our entire life quarry.

DNA might seem very mystic,
Deoxyribonucleic acid,
A string of proteins which control our characteristics.

Our heritage is also not so different,
We may think that we are not related,
But we are much more indifferent.

Our earliest common ancestor was Lucy,
A primate from Africa,
Whose children and kin decided to trek across the blue seas.

And thus, this leads us to our earliest history,
The unfortunate British Empire,
A deadly and gruesome mystery.

Where half of the world was in their control,
The countries of India, the Americas, Egypt, etc.
The countries that had been stolen for resources such as
gold and coal.

The fight for independence took centuries,
The downfall on the 1st of July 1997,
When Hong Kong was handed back to the Chinese after
years of treachery.

But even now wars are carried out by criminals,
For one single reason,
Because of the 1% that makes us all... individuals.

Amogh Nagendra (15)

Fight For Your Rights

Think about the rights you deserve;
To love, speak your mind and to serve.
But what about the ones you don't get?
Let's talk about women's rights, of which many forget.
Women have dealt with sexism throughout the years,
And lots have given blood, sweat and tears.

Sporting has many rules, and unfairly men have had full possession of the ball.
No pay for brilliant sportswomen, while men are getting hundreds of pounds for each win.
Many boys dream of being footballers while, due to tradition, girls are told to be 'perfect daughters'.

Schooling is another, believe it or not but many countries only teach girls how to be a good mother.
In others girls aren't even taught, now that's a battle surely to be fought.
Although it's got better in most, riots are still happening and the government is only about if it will be exposed in the evening post.

As girls grow up they are taught to stay away from 'dodgy' men,
To not be 15 and become the mother hen.
Some seek help and are given alarms, while others shout but are trapped in someone else's arms.

No one should go through this disgrace,
But these things shouldn't have ever happened in the first place.

There are different scales of sexism, it ranges from missing opportunities to bad experiences with men.
It should never have happened and needs to be stopped.
Although things are getting better, why is it taking so long for the world to stop what truly upset her?

Fearne Sutton (13)

Golden Gears, Overcome Fears

As the longing days fled into years,
An ocean of rust flooded my gears...

A story of tears and joy,
Of trust and betrayal,
Of adventure and fatigue.
As souls withered,
Withered, withered,
Away.

Fidgeted frantically, held hopefully,
My face clutched closely to your heart,
As the train tracks rattled,
As the screeching whistle slammed against ears,
And the earthquake beneath you built.
"Time flies. We'll soon be out of this mess,"
You quoted optimistically.

The hall was an awkward place full of awkward people -
You grasped my golden chain,
They turned their backs coldly, muttering resentful tones -
You slipped me in your pocket,
From then they were your very keepers -
You kept me in your lockbox.

As the days washed away,
To your tales of despair and delight,
As the memorable weeks merged into months,
You overcame fears and opened to friends,
And as the months met years, I noticed
You changed: broken to brave
Defeated to determined.

On that day, that Tuesday, the eighth of May,
When the radio said the war had ended,
When Churchill announced normal life shall be ascended,
When freedom and misery flowed,
And the tears splashed and rippled,

"It's time to go home," you told me...
"Or time to leave my home?"

Just like a castle, built on the sand,
Which stands still, tall and fair,
That starts to crumble,
Then washes away to sea,
This large part of your life,
Is but a washed memory,

With dialled numerals encased in gold,
A story imprinted in bold,
As the longing days fled into years,
An ocean of rust flooded my gears.

Aanya Saxena (11)

Madhouse

Clocks that tell the time too late,
Or maybe set to the wrong time zone.
Soft chairs which lull and soothe you till you drop,
Or maybe strap and zap you asleep.
Stairs which lead to nowhere but dead ends,
Or maybe the exit was sealed off.
The madhouse makes no sense.
Or maybe it does, just no one understands yet.
Or maybe they do and they just don't want to.
The madhouse makes no sense.
What to say? Not much.
Well, that's a lie but... now it's the truth.
Why am I here? I don't know. Or maybe I do.
Why am I here, why am I here?
The answer's simple really.
I am mad, insane, off the rocker as they said.
Or at least I wasn't normal.
Not at all is what they said.
My thoughts, my feelings, my opinions
Singled me as an abnormality it seemed,
Because no one else thought the same.
Or at least, anyone who did said nothing.
Nothing. Nothing to say and nothing said.
Nothing to challenge and nothing new to comprehend.
And thus 'normality' remains.

The madhouse makes no sense.
Each resident blabbering incoherent dribble
Most commonly labelled as a madman's preachment.
Nothing to hear. White noise in a black and booming world.
These madmen make no sense.
Or maybe they do and no one understands yet.
Or maybe they do and they just don't want to.
What to say? Not much.
Well, that's a lie but... now it's the truth.
It has to be the truth. No options are left.
A madman's cry could never leave the madhouse.

Taminah Ahmed (14)

Into Folklore

It's not safe to walk the streets anymore,
Let alone drive a car.
For if we were there that day,
We too, might be living on a star.

One bed in your terrace,
Having to make do and mend.
Sharing that bed with your mother,
The other being her boyfriend.

Your own father trying to abduct you,
Yet the timing missed its cue.

A rainy morning caromed its way in,
The bathroom streaming with mildew and plants.
"C'mon, John. It's time to go,"
The voice belonged to your aunt.

Your mother, such a poor soul,
"If only I was there."
She never saw the car approaching,
17 hit, and life crumbled into despair.

Not anymore,
All those feelings have been washed upon the shore.

All that sympathy did good for you,
It helped you 'love' another.

That 'love' that manipulated, hurt your emotions,
You thought of her as your mother.

Your final year was tragic,
Abhorrent to its core.
The gunshot fired, you cried, "I'm shot!"
And your memory has turned into folklore.

I know it was painful,
As Chapman's eyes were disdainful.

I imagine you are in heaven now,
As everything said is true.
But a question everybody is puzzled on is:
I wonder where she keeps you?

Cleo Perry (13)

POV: You're A Woman

Society has standards. Unrealistic ones, unfair ones.
A woman shall be a certain way
They must be fit for a museum display
Not too thin, not too flat, an hourglass waist and frame
All of them shall look the same.

Go work out, cake your face with makeup so that you're
unrecognisable, anything to look perfect, right?
No sugar, no oil, stick to salads and greens
Do what you're told, you're no more than an object
Be size zero, double zero, the smaller the better
Make sure you can fit into the smallest-sized sweaters.

Curly hair? Straighten it. Straight hair? Curl it.
You're so close to being perfect that now you can't quit.
Now thicken your lips, better curves and be toned in all
places
And that old, measly version of yourself? Make sure to leave
no traces.

There, you're perfect now, the most beautiful version of
yourself.
Now you'll finally be happy, free as you can be
It doesn't matter if you have to run to the car because
you're scared,
That you can't leave the house without the fear of being
stared.

Or if you get cat-called just because of what you wore
You look beautiful so it doesn't matter that your heart is torn.
Nobody cares, as long as you look well
How damaged you are, in your broken shell.

Mehnaz Alam (12)

Rupert The Third

I think my cat is a mobster.

I've never heard his meow or his little cries for attention;
He acts without it, exists completely without my permission,
But I'm too scared to correct him,
So I just feed him and watch him meander around like he owns the place.

He might just own the place.
I don't speak cat.

My cat has a posse; a little ginger cat his protégé,
I wonder about their adventures sometimes and then decide
That what happens in the meow-fia, stays in the meow-fia.
I'm not willing to be an accomplice to such things,
Though I suppose I'm already implicated.

I feed him anyway.
Because he's still my cat.
My little black and white mobster with no meow, but a dazzling gaze.

The ginger cat acts as an intermediary, I determine,
Watching him tentatively snack on some of the food I left out
for my little Meow Capone.
Sleek and young, eyes fresh and new;

Lithe movements complementing
the old but tired gait of my cat.

I don't feed the ginger;
He's not my cat. Never has been.
But my tuxedo-clad cat feeds the ginger anyway,
And it feels a little like a game of tug of war.

And at once, when my cat's gone, I watch the ginger cat
walk as he did;
Silent like he was,
Looking at me with the same eyes,
As he escorts me from place to place,
And I know my cat's far too stubborn to just up and leave
his little mob.

Cody Campbell (18)

Lost

I loved the way we lost ourselves in each other,
The way my stomach would still churn with butterflies the
moment you set your blue eyes on me.
Your smoke-scented cologne that would linger on my
cardigan after our embrace,
My notebooks filled with your handwriting, messages of our
adoration and adventures written as though it was history.
That day when your hand was in mine,
Where we skipped classes and wandered across the village,
no cares in the world.
Maybe that's when I realised that my heart was yours.
I know it's hard to imagine, all my love in one boy, I know it's
hard to comprehend, but please, take my love nevertheless.
Yet, weeks later you were a mess, dark circles haunting your
eyes, and the grin that I loved absent on the face I adored.
And as though painted with oil, my hand slipped from yours,
no longer did we escape from the prison we called school.
The softness in your ocean eyes had hardened, and I
couldn't help but cower slightly.
Where was the boy I loved?
Where was the boy who I'd lost myself to?
And you moved on, the path ahead of you was clear.
But you left me at the roundabout, still circling, wondering
which road I should take.

You left me with my tears turning to waterfalls, with my heart unable to be bandaged.
I loved the way we lost ourselves to each other.
But I hate the way I am still lost in you.

Dawn

Reflections Vs Masks

We all know reflections.
We see them all the time.
In that mirror you take thousands of pictures in front of,
In that shiny window in your bedroom,
Or maybe it's on the blank screen of your phone.
But these are not the type of reflections I'm talking about.
Does your reflection show who you are inside?

Don't know what I'm talking about?
Well...
Maybe you are the definition of Eurocentric beauty.
Big blue eyes,
Blonde straight hair,
Porcelain skin that even the sun cannot touch due to its
heavenly texture.
You are also loved by everyone.
Therefore, you must be nice to everyone,
Flashing your pearly white teeth at everyone who
acknowledges your existence.

Or are you just pleasing your followers?
You are their entertainer; they are your audience.
You are the shepherd; the others are sheep.
By day, you wear a mask putting on your fakest smile.
By night, you take it off, revealing your true nature.
Like a lion waiting to attack its prey.

Is this a bad thing?
Not necessarily.
But you are lying to yourself.
Trying to be something you are not.
Therefore, this links back to my question.
Does your reflection show who you are inside?
At the end of the day, you are either Team Reflection
Or Team Mask.
You are free to choose whichever one you like.
But just remember...
Behind a mask lies a person who has no reflection of
happiness.

Favour Emasealu (15)

A Heavy Blue Bag

My blue bag was falling off my shoulders that first day,
Too heavy for a girl unaware of what was to come.
The pockets were begging for books to fill them,
Teach them what it meant to be a woman.

I had sat in that cold classroom, waiting
For strangers to enter and never leave.
Yet their company is finite, so now I'm saying goodbye,
Not to those strangers, but to the people who guided me
from innocence to maturity.
Forever etched into my being.
Marks that can only leave me when I'm ash once more.

I had wandered aimlessly, like a child in a new world.
I suppose that is what I was.
A small thing among the future creators.
The people who passed me could become anyone.
They were everything I wanted to become.
All at once I was submerged in a blank canvas.
The future was my own.

Now my canvas is full, full of more than knowledge,
More than what I thought I knew to be true,
For I never did know much that very first day.
That foolish girl with the heavy bag didn't know that English
was more than question marks and semi-colons,
Letters on a page.

She now knows that everything is more than it seems.
This daunting building, with the big chair by the big door
became a home to me,
And though I may be a blink within its existence,
A nothing within its everything,
I yearn to be remembered, and so I will.

Neave Rees (16)

I Wonder

I wonder if the sky knows how beautiful it is.

I wonder if it knows...
How gorgeous it appears,
When it blushes the prettiest of pink,
In the later afternoon.

I wonder if it knows...
How sublime it appears,
When it flashes striking blue,
Without a cloud in sight.

I wonder if it knows...
How bewitching it appears,
When the sun no longer shines,
And gleaming stars dance before my eyes.

And when the heavens open,
And misery drowns the day,
It still appears beautiful,
Even if it doesn't know it.

I wonder if you know how beautiful you are.

I wonder if you know...
How gorgeous you are,
When you smile the widest of smiles
Without a shred of misery in sight.

I wonder if you know...
How sublime you are,
When your beauty radiates like the sun,
On a cloudless day.

I wonder if you know...
You are as enchanting as the starry skies,
Enlightening everyone you encounter,
Shining like the brightest of stars.

And even when tears dampen your cheeks,
And misery drowns your day,
You are still beautiful,
Even if you don't know it.

Ruby Kedzierski (13)

Hope

'Hope'... What is it?
It's not the choice to change something.
It's not the move that can make things better.
It's believing that if you try hard enough,
You look for the outcome,
That there will be a day
Because that day will be when you look back,
You're able to tell yourself...
'I have hope'.

Otherwise you are nobody.
You always will be everything that has ever been discarded.
That nothing you say or do will be heard or listened to.
That if you achieve something incredible you'll get no
outcome.
It will destroy you,
Make you feel like you are nothing,
That you'll never achieve anything truly amazing.
If you know how to live past that
Then, my nobody...

That's when you have hope.

Plus nobody,
No one will ever be able to stop you from doing what you
believe is right.
That my nobody is hope,

That you can look back at the people who dragged you
down,
Now you can finally ask them...
What is hope?
And if they can't answer that simple question

Then you, my nobody, are the definition of hope...
And nobodies all around will no longer be overshadowed
By the past nor the future.
My hope... My hope is, if you're willing to stand together,
Do so for a brighter future.

Hannah Brown (14)

The Snake

I trod into darkness,
The alley, the dark abyss.
I sought my old friends,
The means to all my ends:
That is what I needed,
Imagination.

A glint in the night,
The corner of my sight,
I stagger to it,
Trip, begging for it.

Its length curls around me,
Squeezing, crushing me.
Tight, my throat is dry and
Its throat opens wide,
Crashing into my side,
Venom leaking through me.

Seeing that I am satisfied,
It snakes itself by my side,
And slips down within me,
Nestling into my debris.
Now I am theirs today.
And sweet sights shall allay.

My snake squirms,
Inside my skull.
Its slim and stark scales,
Encircling my senses,
Scratching my synapses:
Shaping my thoughts;
I lust for its lifeblood.

I relent, and swipe the
Gilded chalice before me.
The sultry, sanguine blood,
Over the rim, it has flood.

A second drips by,
As I grip the glass,
And a tiny fly,
Flutters above the glass.

I take a sip
And feel my mind drip,
Squeezed by the snake,
Coiled tightly to forsake
My head, trapped there.
Feeling: pleasant, bare.

The snake laps up its meal,
Leaving nothing for me to steal.
Yet, and yet. I lust for more,
The snake coiling forevermore.

June Chilvers (17)

Sir William Reeves

You've probably never heard the story,
Of William Reeves' knighthood glory,
A record that was no easy task,
No simple sip from a hot coffee flask,
He started off in Barbados as a zero,
But with help from others became a hero,
Was given the opportunity to study alone,
In England when Victoria was on the throne,
This, the first stepping-stone to his fame,
Studied at Middle Temple for only one reason:
No, not his brains and smarts are to blame,
But his friends of the black community who helped fund,
The required pay, otherwise his education was treason.

In 1863, he returned to his home to achieve new goals,
And would serve Barbados in three different roles:
One as Solicitor-General;
Another as Attorney General;
And the third as Chief of Justice.

His success within Barbados was to be preyed upon,
By England, a larger, stronger and more powerful fish,
Something any educated Victorian boy would wish,
To be admitted to the Queen's Counsel in eighty-three -
A place no one of the time would predict he'd be!

And that's the whole of Sir William Reeves' story,
To how he reached his infamous knighthood glory.

Fraser Hodges-Miner (15)

Social Media

My anxiety takes over
As I press the button labelled 'post'
My intrusive thoughts invade my mind
Like a dictator conquering an innocent country
The pressure starts to build up
Do they like it?
Is it good?
Did I make a mistake?
All of these questions compel me to take it down
I am a slave to other users of social media
Constantly trying to cater for their entertainment needs
Constantly striving for perfection
Constantly impressing others
But does this benefit me?
Inside I desperately cling to the lid of my personal Pandora's box
Filled with anxiety, insecurities and so much more
Tears fall slowly
Hiding behind my screen
I break down slowly
Hiding behind my screen
Innocent, lost
Hiding behind my screen
Once a little girl
Next, still a little girl plastered in make-up

Forced to grow up
I was trapped
Nowhere to go
In the grasp of social media claws
Nobody knows my pain
Truly knows it
The wilderness of social media is ruthless
Be careful.

Khloe Akurang (14)

A Girl In The Mirror

I look in the mirror,
At the girl in front,
I smile
And she does the same
But the smile drops
As her mask slips
And tears suddenly fall.

I don't recognise the girl in the mirror,
She is not me,
Her eyes don't glow,
Her smile doesn't shine,
She looks tired and numb,
But people don't realise that
She is too good at hiding it.

Tears come streaming down my cheeks,
And I take a deep breath,
Wipe my tears away,
And smile,
Not a true smile,
Not one where my eyes glow,
Or my smile shines,
Just a smile
To bury all my feelings inside.

I am a girl in pieces,
A girl in tears,
A girl in pain,
I am no longer recognisable,
I look in the mirror,
And am shocked to see such a stranger,
I don't have my true smile,
Or my sparkly eyes,
Just this mask of a personality.

I feel broken,
And I feel deflated,
I feel so tired,
I feel I am a girl in pieces,
A girl in tears,
A girl in pain.

Elsa Butcher (13)

The Thief

It messed up your days and messed up your nights
Time became a blur.
It sucked your words right from your mouth
Your words became a slur.
Slowly, it imprisoned you
You were gone before you left.

But it's not just memories it steals from your soul,
It gives you unwanted ones
Unwillingly replacing the ones it stole,
Leaving your mind to be like a black hole.
Slowly, it imprisoned you
You were gone before you left.

It turned your joy to sadness and fear;
Fear that your world was becoming less clear
It stole your independence a little more each day
We wished so helplessly as it stole you away.
Slowly, it imprisoned you
You were gone before you left.

One straggling memory wanders by
But it's altered and not quite the same as it is in my mind.
I notice as her mind drifts away
Wondering if she will remember me the next day.
Slowly, it imprisoned you
You were gone before you left.

It hurts when I see you now
Explaining who I am
Because I know I am your granddaughter
But you have forgotten you are my gran.
Finally, it had imprisoned you
You had not left me yet, but you were now gone.

Jessica Smith (17)

Poison

Sexism, a poison in our veins,
A plague that refuses to wane,
A belief in superiority,
Based on gender, a travesty of priority.

Men and women, we stand equal,
Yet sexism seeks to make us feeble,
It defines roles based on our sex,
Limiting our potential and checks.

Women face the brunt of this hate,
Reduced to objects of lust and bait,
Judged by appearance, not their skill,
Their voices ignored, their opinions still.

Men too, suffer from this curse,
Bound by societal expectations, they rehearse,
Emotions suppressed, their worth tied to power,
A toxic masculinity, a society's scour.

We must rise above these gender lines,
Break free from these divisive confines,
Our strength lies in our diversity,
A collective force, a beautiful complexity.

Let us dismantle this system of hate,
Embrace equality, love and celebrate,
A world where every voice is heard,
Where our worth is not tied to our gender.

Amber Urquhart (12)

Release

The gates to the garden are open,
I see the succulent fruit.
I float over to it, feet barely touching the ground.
I feel it in my palm, engrossed by its iridescence.

I take a bite.
The first bite in eight months.
A million flavours dance around my mouth, lingering on my tongue.
Flavours of healing, and opportunity.
The taste is fresh and rejuvenating.

I once was a vessel of hatred and envy,
But I have since dropped my load.
Washed away in a sea of tranquillity,
A deep blue stirring calm.

I take the fruit in armfuls.
I drop it into a pot, its sonority quilting my ears.
The aroma of peace tantalises my senses, a euphoric state of dreams,
As it bubbles and boils, flowing over the pot's rim.

As I eat, I realise clandestinely,
I am an erudite of harmony.

And as my reverie fades,
I find myself reeling in the taste of long-lost merriment.
Exhilaration stinging my lips.

Jessica Russell (14)

Man Kind?

Decades later,
and here we are,
preaching and remembering the same tragedies
caused by man's brutalities.

Over six million lives lost,
years of fighting, years of exhaust.
Picked from the bunch, one by one
no reason, no abnormalities,
no need, no technicalities.

So why do we talk to you today?
Why do we continue to remember the lives taken away?
The answer is,
despite the media and attention,
there doesn't seem to be much of a prevention.

Life after life,
country after country,
no single soul has the right to run free.
Cambodia, Armenia, Bosnia and Herzegovina.
Hundreds more unknown,
how could a person do this to one of their own?

Some sort of greed for power,
a greed for force,
no sight of regret,

no sight of remorse.

Genocide is real,
genocide was real yesterday,
and genocide will still be real tomorrow.

Rosie Woodvine (16)

The Eating Disorder

People think it's glamorous to be skinny
Hide the truth from society
Causing too many insecurities

It isn't fair to be compared
To a standard that can't be reached
Aiming too high
To fall too low
Letting the expectation of an impossible perfection grow

Calorie counting, skipping breakfast
Looking at yourself in the mirror with looks of disgust
Trying to recover feels like the trickiest
Every gain on the scale makes you treat yourself unjust
It isn't right to be afraid
With every pound gained to feel betrayed
It isn't right to feel guilty when you eat
To look at imperfection and feel the need to compete

Throwing up whenever you eat food
To think you've gained weight affects your mood
Not letting a single meal remain in your body
To the point where you start fainting
The guilt you feel to know you contribute to food wasting

Here's a message to those who can relate
You're not alone, you are enough,
You can beat this.

Ahlaam Nur (13)

When You Bombed Us Back Into The Stone Age...

The words get stuck in my throat,
I cannot speak them.
They reverberate within my mind, echoing and screaming.
Can you hear me screaming?

Can you hear me choking on my own blood?
Ferrous and foul.
Can you see it pooling crimson?

Can you see the marks on my skin?
Blossoming purple, like a deadly flower.
They spell out words.
Words of malicious intent.

Can you read these words?
I cannot.
Long ago, my people could.

Long ago we strung letters into words, into books, into greatness.
We laid the foundations to modern life.
We led all innovation.
Now we do not.

Now we are suffocating under the rubble,
Burning under the flames,

Can you smell the corpses?

Rotting and rancid?
Are you choking on the smell,
As it fills your lungs?
As you look at the countless mounds of rushed, forgotten
graves.

Who am I?
I am one of those,
In the mounds.

Who am I?
You do not know?
How could you ever forget?
Who am I?

I am one of the half a million.

Aisha Naushahi Hasan (16)

Who Am I?

Every person tells me what to do.
I don't want to
But I have to
Since I'm a people pleaser.

Hold on, hold tight,
They say they are helping
But in reality
They are making you discreet.

They make me go low
Both status and identity
Why am I here?
Who am I even?

If I don't say it
It's not life
If I do say it
Now it's a life.

Society wanted to shut me up
But they can't
I'm physically existing
They can't push me easily.

"I'm sorry, Mum"
"I'm sorry, Dad"

No, I'm not sorry
I'm sorry for myself.

I want a voice
I want to be heard
I just want to live
Is it really that hard?

If I don't talk
Lie low, shut up
I'm just everyone.

I want to shine
I want to live.

Sophia Cheung (12)

Fit In Or Fit Out

Fit in or fit out
Some people say you need to fit in to be normal,
But what if I can't?
What if I'm made to fit out?
Would that mean I'm meant to be different to all my
friends?
Maybe,
But what if the real me can do both?

Fitting in with the rest of your lot is not as easy as it sounds.
It won't work well with some.
Well, it does not work for me, I've tried many times.
I'm always tagging along behind my friend group,
Or not being able to wear the same things as them because
of insecurities,
Or even trying to say something funny,
But no one laughs.
Maybe I do just fit out.

Difficulties will come around,
Words may sting like nettles,
But at least I'm being the person that's ME.
Sometimes that's difficult,
Sometimes I feel I will always be judged for tiny things I do
differently.
Get called lame or uncool,
Get called weird or different,

But at least different is me.
Me just fits out.

Kitty Cochrane (14)

The Stars Have My Condolences

I stare into the eye of the angel,
Admiring her distant presence,
She's almost transcendental,
Exempt from interference,
In the sky that remains untouched.
But wait...
Why's she moving so much?
Why is her dress suddenly green and red?
She's leaving an unusual trail
Have I been misled?
I thought maybe it was her veil,
But smoke pollutes the air,
Tears of betrayal, they fill my eyes
For how they had deceived me was so unfair.
If she should speak, the poor angel should cry...
She watches as we corrupt,
Disturbing the poor universe
That was once left untouched
Until now, until its very last verse.

Now staring at the scattered stars,
That bathe in infinite depths of beauty,

I notice they're corrupted by our planes and cars
And to see her in her misery,
It filled me with condolence.

Sophie Watson (13)

The World's Biggest Mysteries

The one thing I hate the most in this world,
Anyone could go...
From sitting at home
Hiding inside; beknownst to the snow -

To vanishing away from the face of Earth.
Off to a place that no one knows.

As I sit and read the history,
Those who are remembered as:
'The world's biggest mysteries'
Madeleine McCann, Rebecca Coriam, Mary Flanagan
Time begins to fade away. Losing their integrity
Lord Lucan, Teddy Wang, Ben Needham
Locating their whereabouts? The job is contradictory

So, despite our developed intelligence,
Loved ones are missing and not found.
Our government is obsessed with profit.
Money! Investments! Pounds!
Always the families flocking in fear -
No support nor any care.
But that's okay, isn't it?
As long as they boost the economy...
No matter who, what or where;

They don't have to be safe and sound.
It's just like they're not here, or like they never were.

Alicia Geere (15)

Practice Makes Perfect

Practice makes perfect,
But everything is imperfect,
Perfect isn't real,
Like overpriced meal deals.

You practise and practise,
But keep failing and failing.
You start to become in disbelief,
And never hit that sense of relief
But still, you keep trying.

Thoughts run around your head,
Till you would rather be dead.
All this starts to mean nothing,
All your dreams are crushing.

You try to do your best,
You're trying your hardest,
But it always leads to failure.

You'll get it if you just keep practising,
So, you practise and practice till it's damaging
But still you're failing,
All this failure leads to hatred,
Hatred towards it and to yourself,
Everything else around you has faded.

Your best can never be the best,
Thinking you're just average towards the rest,
Practising never works out,
It just puts you in doubt.

Practice doesn't make perfect
Practice makes nothing.

Venita Kamara (14)

Night

The darkness of night,
Slowly creeps upward in its might,
Engulfing the world with its cloak,
Land disappearing from sight, in its yoke.

The serene stars aglow above,
Shine bright, showering love,
The still, caring moonlight,
Lends an enchanting sight.

The lights of the city flicker and glow,
As the winter wind feels gritty and slow,
The streets in a blanket of snow,
Evening was pretty, but night begins to grow.

The shadows of daylight,
Run off to play in sheer delight,
Into the dark, they love to stray,
But avoid the snow, white as they sway.

I see my own shadow joining the fray,
As darkness wraps around like a cloak to stay,
Our human minds, so used to light,
Take a moment to evoke, the beauty of the night.

As our minds soak in its wondrous might,
Let us revel in the darkness, with all our might,
For the night, in its beauty, makes me strong,
But it only lasts so long.

Rushaananth Srirankan (13)

The Monster Under My Bed

The monster under my bed
It keeps things running through my head
I toss and turn
But all my thoughts seem to burn
I feel like I can never escape
Things keep me up: my words, my shape

The monster under my bed
It's holding me by a thread
It makes me feel like a burden
But I can never be certain
How long does it take for it to see
That sometimes it breaks me

The monster under my bed
It makes me think of things I've never even said
I can only think of times I messed up
Not of the proud moments that fill a whole cup
It won't let me grow wings and take flight
Even if I do everything right

The monster under my bed
It won't leave no matter how many tears I shed
When will I learn
It's there at every turn

Whatever I've done to get rid of it
It doesn't even count one bit

I am the monster under my bed
Oh how many times have my words bled?

Emilia Biondi (13)

A Monochrome Spectrum

What is it that makes a colour?
What contrasts yellow and blue?
Is it the splitting of light?
The difference of frequency?
Personal preference?
Or what others tell me?

What makes something red?
The blossom of a naive romance?
Or the burning sensation of anger?
Is it the thickness of blood
When mine has worn so thin?

What makes something white?
Is it rays of the sun's light?
Is it the fragileness of innocence and purity?
Is it a privilege that I haven't earned?

What exactly is black?
The absence of colour?
The mixture of all?
Is it a deep loneliness or despair
Or is it centuries of isolation and prejudice?

What is it that makes a colour?
Honestly, I don't know,
In a world of blues, yellows, reds and whites.

Avomo-Mbasogo Mba Ngumea (14)

The Villain's POV

A hero is what I aimed to be,
Yet a villain is what they named me.
I never had a chance to prove myself,
It's as if my book was already on the shelf.

I never used to be like this,
Then all of a sudden, I met my nemesis.
Life itself took a swing at me
And decided I should never be free.

My hands are bound and I can't escape
My mind is screaming but my voice is taped.
My heart is battered and bruised like never before
Life took my will and locked it in the drawer.

The villain is blamed for all of life's flaws,
Even though none of them they did cause.
Life comes out looking like the winner
And the villain is put down for being the sinner.

In reality, oh how the plot is twisted
Life sucks its soul and pretends it never existed.
He goes ahead and takes all the glory,
So the villain will always be the villain as the hero tells the
story.

Asma Abdi (16)

GCSEs

The drip of the tap
The tap of the drips
The snip of the snap
And the snap of the snip
The clock ticking
The tick-tocking
The pens clicking
And the click-clacking
Of the shoes that will bring
The paper to my table
I hope, oh I hope, I hope I don't fail.

My palms sweaty
And my throat hoarse
"Did I study enough? Oh no... I'll fail the course!"
The clicking and clacking of the shoes of the lady
Bringing my anxiety closer to its source,
What do I do, what do I do?
I frantically think
If I run now, I'll be gone in a blink.

But I sit still and wait for my turn
And the clicking of the pens makes my stomach start to churn
What now? What now? It's far too late!
So I sit the exam and now I can deflate

Well, until the results come rolling in
Because I'm very sure, I'll get a grounding.

Taylia Edy (16)

The Forgotten War

World War 2 was a tragedy,
That we remember to this day,
But over time, the First World War,
Has just seemed to fade away.

We acknowledge the soldiers,
Who in 1939,
Fought and lost their lives,
Remembered for all time.

But those Great War deaths,
Took just as much strength,
Yet somehow, they're not as recognised,
Though we won 'coz of those men.

Although Poppy Day, originally,
Marked the end of World War 1,
Number 2 is more remembered,
Though both wars, we won.

If we're forgetting the first,
Who says we won't forget again,
If war's consequences aren't remembered,
What will happen then?

History will repeat,
More innocents slain,

A future filled with blood,
Misery and pain.

So, remember these wars,
And all others across the seas,
So, our mistakes aren't repeated,
And we can live our lives in peace.

Tamara Kramer (13)

Cell Phone

Why is it called a cell phone?
Our phones,
Our life support.
This mobile device,
Breathes the air into our lungs,
Keeps us alive.
Wires of computers,
Tethered to our veins.
Break the connection,
And it's all over.
This futile attempt to quench our insatiable hunger,
Our insatiable hunger for more.
Keep scrolling,
Feed your mind.
Keep this irrepressible hunger at bay.

Why is it called a cell phone?
The warped conception of reality,
The girls on the Internet.
Too perfect to be true.
Flawless where I am not.
Donning masks to obscure their flaws,
Because perfection is the beauty standard.
They too, are prisoners.
Helpless and vulnerable,
Slaves to our own system.

Wired to self-destruct.
Break through the shackles binding you to your phone,
Relieve yourselves of your burden.

So, again, I ask you, why is it called a cell phone?

Selin Erdogan (12)

Mercy And Forgiveness

Hurt others I had,
Hurt you I did,
Forgiveness I'd seek,
From the world I hid.
From showing no remorse,
To bittersweet guilt.
I ask for your mercy,
From the canal of shame I'd built.

You say, "Forgiveness you shan't receive, you devilish being."
"A grudge still I hold, my mercy bears no meaning."
I dwell in the depths of dark and despair.
I say, "I am undeserving," but my fate shan't be yet.

I rise from my canal of shame,
I am no longer in chains,
I am no longer in pain,
My efforts shan't be in vain.

I say, "Forgive me or forgive me not, it doesn't matter to me."
"It won't stop me from living, I'll advance with glee."
I drain my canal and tear down its walls.
Truly, the forgiveness of oneself is most merciful of all.

Khadija Ali (13)

Bloody Saturday

Mother held his hand tightly
Crossed the shattered street with the others
But he doesn't know why they were rushing.

People crowded on the platform
Waited for the train,
It wasn't the first time he saw that many
Planes buzzed and circled in the gloomy sky,
Dropping tiny planes like fish laying eggs.
Mother was horrified, told him to *run* -
Suddenly the flashing light blinded his eyes
The stinging heat pushed him far away,
Away from his mother
Into the silent land.

A man carried him to safety,
His clothes soaked in red, sky filled with grey;
He coughed in the choky cinders,
Bawled for the burning pain
And searched for his mother in the piles of limbs,
But nothing was left.
Except the noise of sirens and the wailing of the remainers
Depressing like a dirge.

Yunqi Shan (17)

Boys

I used to find it funny to wink at boys
I used to think it was a joke
I used to laugh at cheesy pickup lines
And all the silly looks they would invoke
I used to feel safe walking home
Even at night, even alone

But then the boys started winking back
It was no longer a joke
The words screamed from moving cars
Drained me of my hope
They said my eyes were stars
And I'd look good in their arms
But I was blind to their affection
Their words made walking home alone
Feel like a task requiring protection

I long to go back
Back to the time of harmless winks
And funny pickup lines
To the time of fun and not fear
But I can never go back

Because I no longer think it's funny to wink at boys
Or tell them a cheesy pickup line
The boys stole that from me

And to be honest,
They can keep it.

Lucy Filippini (14)

Imperfection

Imperfect. Ugly. That's what they call me.
Blue alien. Freak. These words kill me.
Don't look at her, she's ugly. They belittle me.
They think I don't have feelings.
But we are the same, you and me.

You think you are better than me,
I think we are equal.
Even though I might be irregular,
And might have some flaws,
That doesn't make me less of a person,
Than I already am.

So get yourself up and stand tall,
Because no one can be better than you,
No one can push you down.
In every unique way,
We are beautiful.
Not alien. Not freak. But human.

Imperfect but human.
That's what we all are.
We all make mistakes, and we all have our faults.
We all think people are better, stronger and greater than us.
But the truth is,
Is that we are all imperfect.

Simi Ajibade (12)

Remember The Word

When the world threatens to drown you,
Burn your skin from your bones
And all that's left for you to do
Is take that knife, gun or leap from stone
Because you're terrified if you spill your secrets and fears
Then you'll be weak and alone.
No one's told you it's okay for there to be tears.
For so long you've been on your own,
Now it's time for you to be shown,
To see the outline of hope in the future,
Near or far, it doesn't matter, the seed's been sown.
Use it for your wounds, give them sutures,
And when that moment arrives grab it,
Hold on tight, don't ever let go.
Remember the good times, and when the bad days hit,
Don't overthink or run or panic, love yourself, take it slow
And know there is always going to be hope.

Amelia Collyer (14)

This Is How...

I was so old when I was ripped from my mother's womb
Shoved and pushed and torn away into
The cold blue.
Reams of paper, frigid, ticking.
This is how I rot.

Sit with the beetle shells in my bathtub,
Peek through the flies on my window.
It's raining.
Wade through the pages,
This is how I wash.

Peeling muscle and a loose eyeball,
Sluggish shuffle from day to night.
Shoulders heavy from my
Bag full of the sun and moon,
This is how I lose my arm.

My brain will leak from my ear,
Thick, pink, paste-like pate.
Trampled by familiar shoes,
Heavy soles, rubber and steel.
This is how I slip away.

I am so old now.
There is nothing these bones can do but grow.
Roses from my ribs,

Lilies from my skull,
Marigolds instead of my tongue.
This is how I live.

Grace Leech (16)

Only In The Tinged Orange Sunset

Sunset,
Nature's golden treasure,
Crisp leaves, dancing daisies, chirping robins.
All dazzle brightly in the autumn light,
Only in the tinged orange sunset,

Tinged orange sunset,
Making the elegant tears on my face,
Gently shiver and glimmer,
Only in the tinged orange sunset,

The undying rage we reap,
The overbearing sorrow we sow.
All of winter's cold-heartedness
Can all be blown away,
With the dainty autumn breeze,
In the tinged orange sunset.

Sunset,
Nature's golden treasure,
Crisp leaves, dancing daisies, chirping robins.
All dazzle brightly in the autumn light,
Only in the tinged orange sunset.

On a tinged orange sunset,
I wait for you,
With pure moistened eyes of joy,
I wait for you,
Only in the tinged orange sunset,
I wait for you.

Daniel Sokunle (14)

The Girl

On the beach there was a girl
With brown eyes and a head of curls
She danced, she skipped, she twirled
And she shone brighter than a pearl

She was so blissful, she ran so well
But then she inevitably fell
She seemed shocked at first, but she did not dwell
She ran on to see some shells

After this she rolled her trousers up above her knee
And sprinted excitedly towards the sea
She danced and she seemed so free
And upon her face was a look of pure glee

There was an aura of joy around her
And she didn't need money or a chauffeur
She needed no title like dame or sir
And was fine with being simply amateur

She was joyous and she was glad
For she found no reason to be sad
And although she never kept up with the latest fad
She was content with what she had.

Ramona Randhawa (12)

Easier Said Than Done...

It's already 2023! Soon it will be 2024,
To 2025, 2026 and many more right?
Well, it might...

The way we're treating the Earth,
I don't think we'll last
We'll be gone in a flash
I'm not wishing for this, I hope no one is

If we had a quiz,
All about this we would say let's save the Earth,
It's easier said than done

In 1999-2010 we thought that by 2022 we'd be using flying cars,
But now in 2023 we're thinking we won't last very long
Do you see the big difference?

We say we're going to change climate change
But it's easier said than done...
Our Earth is fragile, it can't keep up with us
So we say we're going to save the Earth

But it's easier said than done...

Favour Akukalia (12)

Women In This Society

We feel silenced, so alone,
Second class, never at home.
We never have a choice,
Just our do's and don'ts.
Pushed and threatened everywhere we go,
No one will ever know the pain of being a woman in this day
and age.
Even with feminists on our side,
We're still fighting a war for centuries to come,
Against sexism and misogynists and all the idiots which
agree.
They won't educate or train us,
They just torture and rape us,
Because they believe only men can get the fancy degree.
And when he impregnates us,
We can't just abort it,
They want our torture, our nightmare,
To stick by us,
To remind us that all we are is just second class.

Gracie Chapman (13)

Memory

Sticks and stones may break my bones,
But words are what will scar me,
Words said with innocence,
Words said with intent,
They burn their way into my brain,
Blistered in my memory,
Nowhere to run,
Nowhere to hide,
The memory of their words haunts me,
Following me around like a shadow,
I can't run,
I can't hide,
The light that once shone with happiness and hope,
Is now gone,
I am in darkness,
That silly nursery rhyme we were taught as kids,
Was just a fib,
Sticks and stones can break my bones,
But words will never hurt me,
The words don't hurt physically,
They scar you mentally,
They have you in a tight grip,
Suffocating you,
Torturing you,
Burnt into my memory.

Bethany Milner (17)

Dreams

Dreams,
They are like a hope that you have for the future,
They are like a wishing well, you think about what you want
in the future and you throw it into reality.

Dreams,
They are like dice, you throw the idea around your head and
it can have different outcomes.
They are like a window into your life, they show you an
option and you can choose to put that into your life or to
leave it as a fantasy.

I often find myself wondering if dreams are like a
conscience,
They influence the way we see our lives.
I ponder upon the question of why do we need help making
these decisions about our lives.
Does the universe doubt our abilities to think for ourselves?

Grace Davage (13)

Glorious Swans

The wings as white as the clouds
Her beauty pure and true
They graciously swim
They glide across the water elegantly

Have you ever seen a swan?
They're as beautiful as you
Their wings flap making a splash
I wish I could see them

I watch them day and night
Kids run around and play
But I'm not bothered
I sit and play with my clay

I sculpt a swan and paint it white
They put it on display
I reach new heights
And the water glistens

Suddenly flute music plays
The melody so pretty
I replay it in my head
As I lie down and sleep...

Jessica Pavitt (10)

Promises

I promise to clean the dishes
I promise not to frown
I promise to look happy
Even when I'm feeling down

I promise not to drink
And I will go to school
I promise I'll be better
So I don't look like a fool

I promise to be content
And never to feel blue
I promise to keep quiet and
And not tell you what to do

I promise I'm okay
I promise I'm alright
I promise I'll be presentable
And remember to be polite

I promise I won't keep spending
Because I can't afford
But I forget my promise
And buy things because I'm bored

We promise lots of things
We do it as a token
But sometimes promises kept
Are very slowly broken.

Portia Mitchell (14)

Care For Our Planet

C aring is something we all must learn,
A nimals are dying, habitats destroyed.
R ivers, full of discarded plastics,
E ven fields and flowers are not spared.

F ights for freedom and nature cannot prevent,
O ur immoral governments doing wrong.
R ising water levels alike Earth's problems.

T ime is wasted but
H ope still lingers.
E arth, can she be saved?

P eople must believe.
L ush nature, please return.
A nimals, find back your homes, thrive
N urture your offspring carefree.
E arth pleads: stop and care.
T o do right, not wrong, do your share.

Otto Mills-Arends (12)

Parents

Parents have a special place in their child's life
when they can grow and develop through their daily lives
even when their presence always remains even when they
go too far!
No matter how big or successful the parent's child is,
children have grown throughout life and can not be left
unfulfilled and ignored.
Parents bear all the difficulties to nurture their children...
But grown-up adults can't even spare a few seconds to
spend time with them at a later period in life!
Parenting is a special bond that children only understand
when they get the opportunity to play their role!

Benjamin Doeteh (16)

India

India, a tapestry of vibrant hues,
The dancing peacocks, the sapphire blues.
Saffron, green, and white of old,
Linger like in a time of days of yore.
Encompassing the mountains and rivers and land,
Stands a country of beauty and grand.
From the sarees and spices of the north,
To the beaches and waves of the south.
The Taj Mahal and the Ganges flow,
Creating an India that's aglow.
She stands with pride and strength forever,
An ode to her is an endeavour.
So come to this stunning nation,
Experience India in its full creation.
For here stands a land of timeless splendour,
An epicentre of unity and tender.

Niya Kawa (13)

My Happy Place

The adrenaline running through my body,
My heart beating just that little faster
My belly fluttering like there are a thousand butterflies
inside of me.
It's match day, my happy place is on that pitch leading my
team out to the field of play.
It's ninety whole minutes of me being me, doing something
I'm good at.
That whistle goes and it rings in my ears, all the tension
releases from my body, it drains away.
The shoulder to shoulder, the sliding across the ground.
The noise of the crowd shouting my name.
It's 90 minutes, once a week, but those are my minutes to
shine.

Benji Lomax (13)

Grateful

A break-in,
The tiresome storm,
A pause in the forever-calling,
Wind.

Something to be grateful for,
In the darkness,
All the light comes from the sun,

But only a fragment,
Is left for us to shine,
We should all be grateful for,
Even knowledge is never permanent.

Hope makes us grateful,
Knowing that only the fading lilac sky,
Will only bring another day,
Filled with sadness
And teardrops of joy.

I feel as if I could fly
So high,
Reach a branch further,
Float into the clouds and
Dream the night away,

For I am grateful,
For the people I know,
The places I go,
For who I am.

Anushka Rosenberg (14)

Maître De La Langue

There dwells a weapon in each and every one of us.
It's a gift that brings destruction
Or a gift that brings peace
It's a gift that forms allies
And a gift that makes foes
A gift that can cause corruption
And a gift that flowers purity
It's a gift which once you master
Can grant you freedom
I shan't tell you how
Nor what it is
Because what you do with it is your responsibility
It's a fire which you let spread
Or a fire that you control
But never to put out.

George Bracey (12)

Hopeless Romantic

Our hearts yearn backwards,
We crave to be known and seen.

We hope that our searchers have not ceased their search,
That their anguished heart cries to the moon at night in
search of us.

But I no longer desire to be found,
Don't follow me now.

Let's fearfully be,
And trust that one day we cross paths again.

But for now, let the stars be vigilant over us,
Let the present shelter us and the future wait.

We can now go our own ways,
And know that when the stars collide

It will not be my finding,
But a collision of our destinies.

Mexi Wright (14)

I Have My Own Dream

I have a dream...
that all the little white boys and girls
and all the little black boys and girls would come together.
Well, Doctor King, I have my own dream.
I have a dream that the police won't use their job as an excuse to kill innocent people of African and Caribbean heritage.
I have a dream that people like George Floyd will not be killed for being black.
I have a dream that people like Doctor King will not be killed for just standing up for people of African and Caribbean heritage.

Ruth Kaputa (13)

Smudge

S o many cats in the world that don't commit crime
M any more behaved than you in their prime
U nfortunately, you hate them like doors and mimes
D ivorce, dogs, danger was the way I met and obtained
   you through the grime
G reat things have happened to me ever since I got you all,
   like getting that slime
E ven though there are so many cats in the world you
   misbehave and wake me up in the night
I still only choose you as my cat all the time.

Arthur Bannister (13)

The Dead Won't Care

A DNR was placed above her head
A mother of four about to be dead
Yet her mother-in-law won't shut up
About what we're doing afterwards

The funeral location up for debate
Catholic, Church of England or Methodist on the slate
Yet what my mother would've wanted
Is a day about her with nobody to disrupt it

What her mother-in-law doesn't see
Is that my mother has her own family
And if that family was bothered about it
We'd have it in her home town with her birth religion.

Alexis Higham (13)

Climate Change

This land is a constant state of birth,
Giving life to all living on Earth.
Our carelessness and fears
Have taken a toll over the years.

Her land is parched and scorched
As man continues to light the torch.
We continue a want of speed and ease,
All while our pesticides kill off our bees.

It's time to wake up and see Mother Earth's pain.
Humanity's selfishness is becoming insane.
Soon her cries will turn to gloom
And man will cause its own doom.

Vishnu Vardhan Beemu-Padmanaban (12)

That's What Makes You Stronger

They didn't notice you were crying
They didn't notice you were tired
They didn't notice you were alone
They didn't notice how attentive you were
They didn't notice how you actually tried to make others smile.

They noticed your failing grades
They noticed your unattractiveness
They noticed all your flaws.

But you stayed strong
And kept going on.
You never lost hope
And never let them take you down...

That's what made you stronger.

Laiba Mazumder (12)

Roots Of Origin

Roots of origin,
Roots filled with poison endangering my mind,
Although aware of many, this one engraved,
Engraved so deeply it poisons me but yet can't be found.

You are worthless, you are useless
As the word 'worthless' means disposed of, I am not.
Yet it hurts.
Perhaps it isn't a monster of one root,
Perhaps it's a monster of many roots...
Weaved into one being.

Anastasija Popova (15)

Friendship

Friendship is a powerful thing
It brings joy and belief to make your heart sing

Friendship is a necklace of devotion
Made with love and sadness and every other emotion

Friendship has its ups and downs
But it's infinite
Through all bounds

Friendship is about forgiveness
It's as wide as the world
It sparkles in space
Like the moon and stars.

Crystal Onwonga

Littering

Littering is a harmful thing,
We are hurting our animals,
Birds are getting stuck and starving,
Sealife, thinking it is food.
We are killing innocent animals.
Harming the environment,
Littering can lead to pollution,
Littering can lead to the spread of diseases,
Littering is a crime.
So just take the extra minute to put it in the bin.
Help save our planet.

Alicia Barden (14)

The Dandelion

A ball of life,
You give it a blow,
Then make a wish,
And watch the angels flow,
Each tiny seed floating by,
They land, take root and you wonder why,
Such a small tiny thing,
Can create a new beginning,
We all need to do this when we wander,
Sprinkle some seeds to help be surreal
Or make your own dandelion wish,
That our future generations start to feel,
That it's not too late for the world to heal.

Daisy Adela Anderson (13)

Dreams

If you dream the dream
All of your darkest fears will come to life
You will shake and scream
As if there was a knife

But, as you wake up
In your mind
All of your fears will be washed up
And soon you will find

The light inside of you
You will stand up and fight
And you will stay true
Your light will shine bright.

Melissa Foster-Turner (14)

Environment

E veryone takes care of the environment
N ever litter
V alue the environment
I dyllic ice
R otate the world
O rchards are bright
N arwhals are in danger
M onkeys will adopt other monkeys
E agles are very fast
N ewts live in the water
T asmanian devil with pink ears.

Maggie Hodson (13)

I'm Tired

I feel my eyes flutter, heavier than rocks,
M y shoulders slumped, curved like a circle.

T he words around me linger in the air, echoing in my
   mind,
I feel my lips slowly part, my jaw starting to unclench,
R ight before me there are a million words on a sheet,
E ven too tired to try, I feel so tired, it's like I might
D ie.

Taylor Hotchkiss (11)

Greed

Wind rushed through,
The air was cool,
What once was a lively place,
Was as dead as a zombie,
The green grass,
Turned to dry ground,
The chirping birds,
Turned to a deafening silence.
But this wasn't the work of a beast,
No,
Not at all,
It was the work of a human,
A human who only took,
And never gave,
The forest, now completely gone,
Due to selfish acts,
Of us.

Octavia Yvon (11)

My World

I watch the world shape around me
Most things I can't explain
Why can't we have a world that's simple,
And where everybody's treated the same?

A whirl of worries lies ahead of me
Wherever I choose to go
But where is my place in this world,
In a future that sways to and fro?

Aneia Duller (11)

Gone

Gone
Gone away
The ideas of
Conflict and climate change.
Youthful voices are drowned out
Under the drone of an adult's murmur
The world is burning: fire, fire, fire!
No, we will not stand for:
Burning buildings or endless torrents,
Destroyed timberland or droughts,
We hope that
They are
Gone.

Ruby Clark (12)

The Loss

When she died
I cried
Yet I tried
But I lied.

I wanted to be mad
But that was bad
So I tried to be glad
I just ended up sad.

In my bed I lay
Where I wish I could stay
To find a way
To get through the day.

Melanie Dixon (12)

Madness Of Mankind

Darkness descends slowly,
like a blanket, or a cage.
Blades of grass wither
as they turn from green to beige.
Trees vanish suddenly
to forge an inky page.
As nature slowly dies
murdered by the human age.

Anya Bansal (15)

YOUNG WRITERS INFORMATION

We hope you have enjoyed reading this book – and that you will continue to in the coming years.

If you're the parent or family member of an enthusiastic poet or story writer, do visit our website www.youngwriters.co.uk/subscribe and sign up to receive news, competitions, writing challenges and tips, activities and much, much more! There's lots to keep budding writers motivated!

If you would like to order further copies of this book, or any of our other titles, then please give us a call or order via your online account.

Young Writers
Remus House
Coltsfoot Drive
Peterborough
PE2 9BF
(01733) 890066
info@youngwriters.co.uk

JOIN IN THE CONVERSATION!

TIPS, NEWS, GIVEAWAYS AND MUCH MORE!

 YoungWritersUK

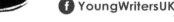 YoungWritersCW  youngwriterscw

 SCAN ME TO WATCH THE POWER OF POETRY VIDEO!